# MAZES 2

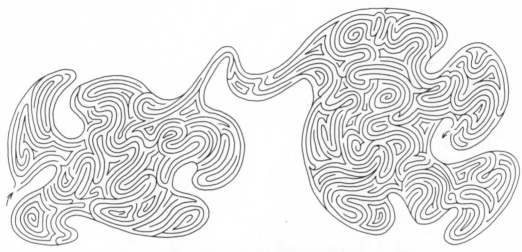

# MAZES 2

## BY VLADIMIR KOZIAKIN

GROSSET & DUNLAP
A NATIONAL GENERAL COMPANY
PUBLISHERS·NEW YORK

*Dedicated to*
   *the dedicated of*
      *Mazes 1,*
         *Marge Ternes*
            *and Jock Bartlett.*

ISBN: 0-448-01829-2

Manufactured in the United States of America

# INTRODUCTION

*Here is the second collection of mazes, graphic puzzles that take their inspiration from the labyrinths of ancient times.*

*The purpose of a maze is simple: Just plunge in and see if you can find your way out without crossing any solid lines. You can time yourself against a friend or, if working alone, against the Rated Time Limit. Remember, though, that time is elusive and highly subjective—you might solve one maze in jig time only to be hung up interminably on another but no more difficult one. If matters get truly desperate the solutions are printed in the back of the book. Don't panic if your solution doesn't agree with the "official" one—some mazes have more than one exit path, but so long as you don't jump any lines, one solution is as good as another.*

*In the introduction to the first collection, tissue paper was suggested as an aid to solving the puzzles. By placing the paper over the maze you can keep the maze clean and reusable. If these puzzles drive you into a rage, put them down and go out and get yourself a copy of the first collection.*

Vladimir Koziakin

*Maze 1*
# PAPILLON
*Rated Time Limit:* | *2 Minutes*

# DIAMOND HEAD

*Rated Time Limit:* | 3 Minutes

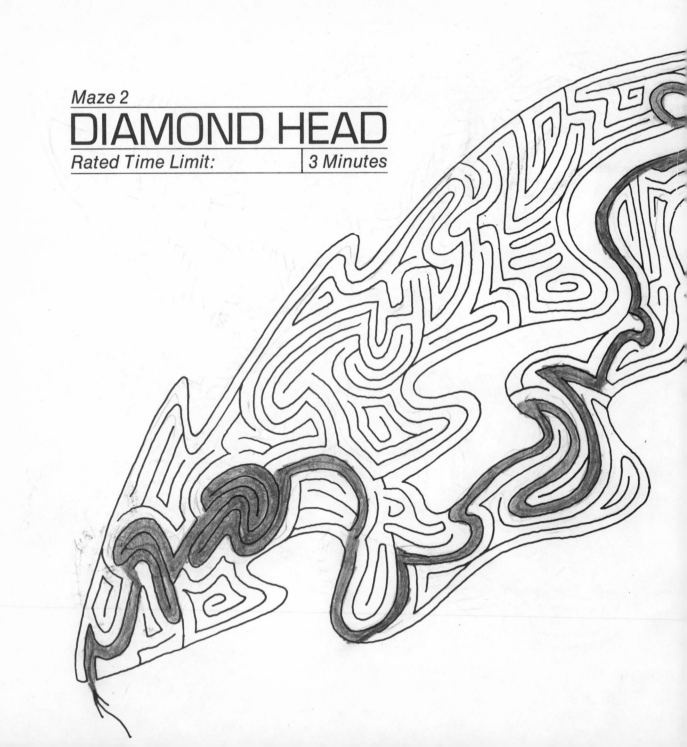

Maze 3
# STIMULUS
Rated Time Limit: | 4 Minutes

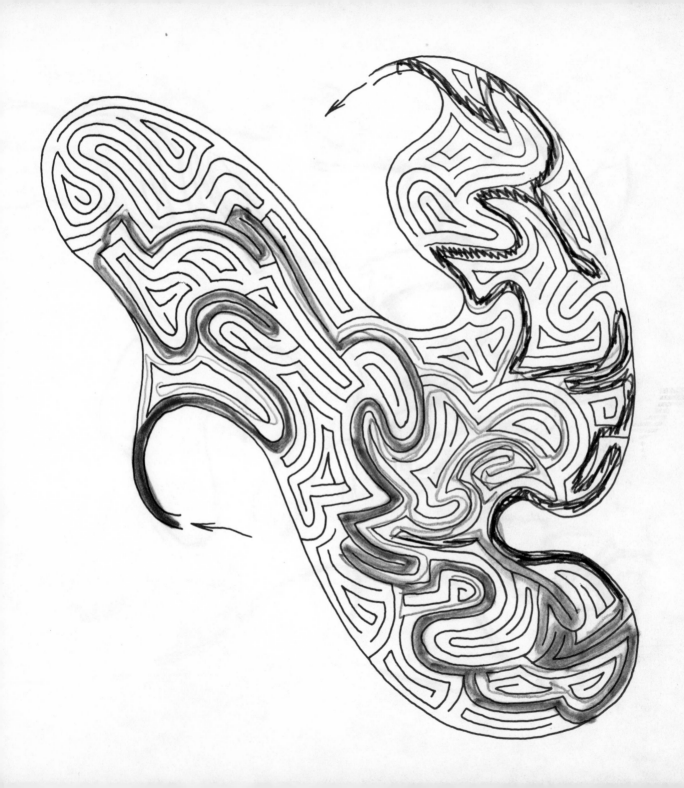

Maze 4
# SNOOPY
*Rated Time Limit:* | 5 Minutes

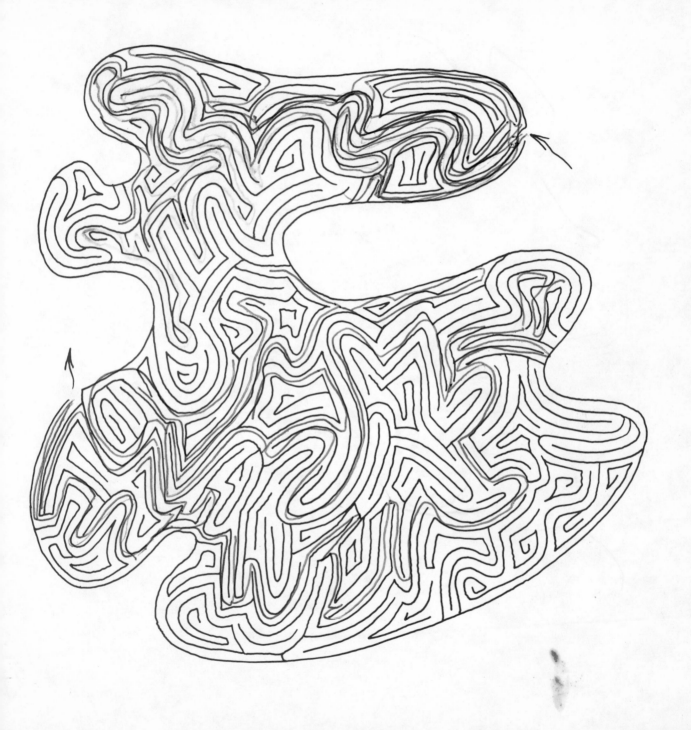

*Maze 5*

# BURLESQUE

*Rated Time Limit:* | *6 Minutes*

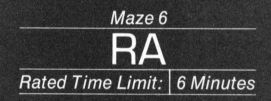

Maze 6
# RA
Rated Time Limit: | 6 Minutes

Maze 7
# ART DECO
*Rated Time Limit:* | 6 Minutes

*Maze 8*
# GREAT STONE FACE
*Rated Time Limit:* | 7½ Minutes

Maze 9

# CYRANO

Rated Time Limit: | 7½ Minutes

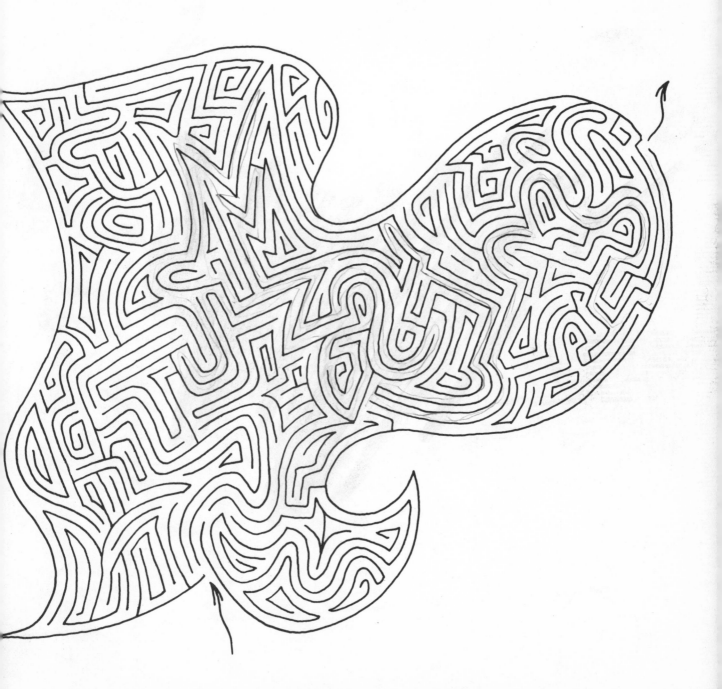

Maze 11

# ZED

*Rated Time Limit:* | *9 Minutes*

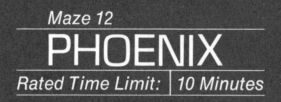

Maze 12
# PHOENIX
Rated Time Limit: | 10 Minutes

11/10/79
5 - 8 mins

*Maze 13*

# HELIOGABALUS

*Rated Time Limit:* | 10 Minutes

Maze 14
# WELCOME BACK
Rated Time Limit: | 12 Minutes

*Maze 15*

# TANNENBAUM

*Rated Time Limit:* | *13 Minutes*

*Maze 16*

# GODZILLA

*Rated Time Limit:* | *13 Minutes*

Maze 17
# SPAGHETTI
*Rated Time Limit:* | *15 Minutes*

Maze 18

# GALAPAGOS TORTOISE

Rated Time Limit: | 19 Minutes

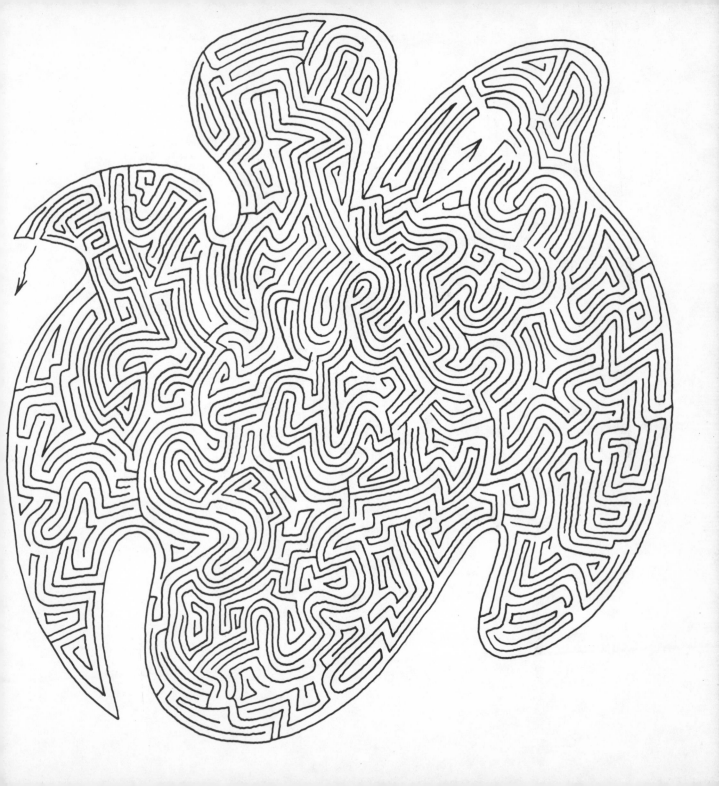

*Maze 19*

# VEGETABLE

*Rated Time Limit:* | *20 Minutes*

Maze 20

# THINK

Rated Time Limit: | 20 Minutes

*Maze 21*

# MARTIAN

*Rated Time Limit:* | *20 Minutes*

Maze 22

# ZEUS

Rated Time Limit: | 20 Minutes

Maze 23
# DOPPELGÄNGER
Rated Time Limit: | 22 Minutes

Maze 24

# ALBERICH

*Rated Time Limit:* | 22 Minutes

Maze 25
# WITHDRAWAL
Rated Time Limit: | 24 Minutes

*Maze 26*

# WALRUS

*Rated Time Limit:* | *24 Minutes*

Maze 27

# SPLAT

*Rated Time Limit:* | *25 Minutes*

Maze 28
# ITZAMNA
Rated Time Limit: | 26 Minutes

Maze 29
# PIRANHA
*Rated Time Limit:* │ *26 Minutes*

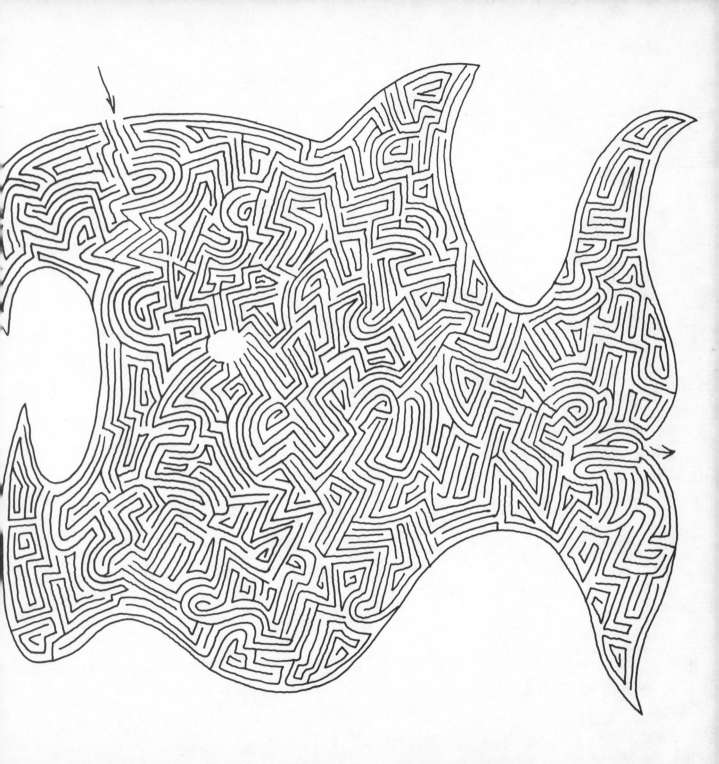

*Maze 30*

# MARE'S NEST

*Rated Time Limit:* | *28 Minutes*

*Maze 31*
# PIGGY
*Rated Time Limit:* | *28 Minutes*

Maze 32

# MENACE

Rated Time Limit: | 30 Minutes

Maze 33

# SCHIZOPHRENIA

Rated Time Limit:   |   32 Minutes

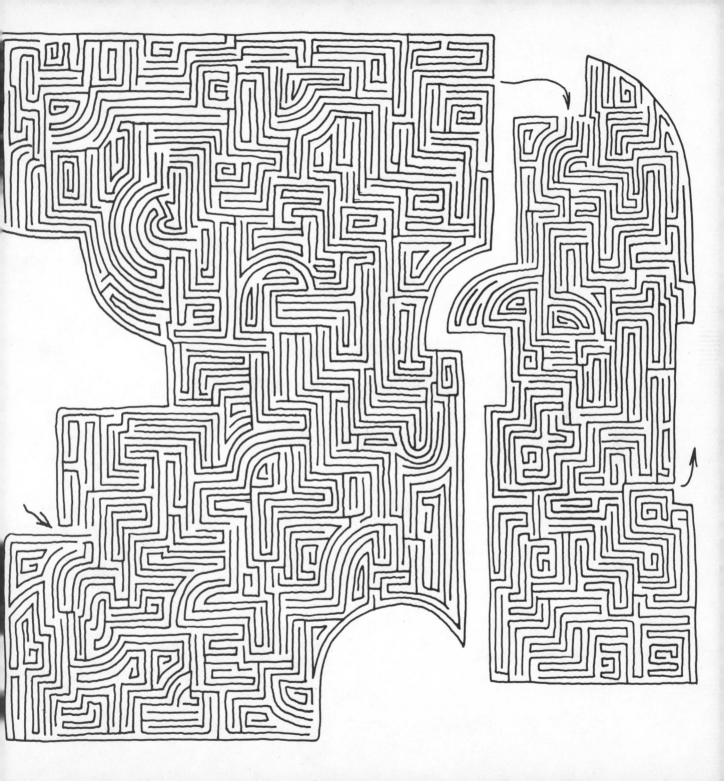

*Maze 34*

# PREMONITION

*Rated Time Limit:* | *32 Minutes*

*Maze 35*

# POPOCATEPETL

*Rated Time Limit:* | *35 Minutes*

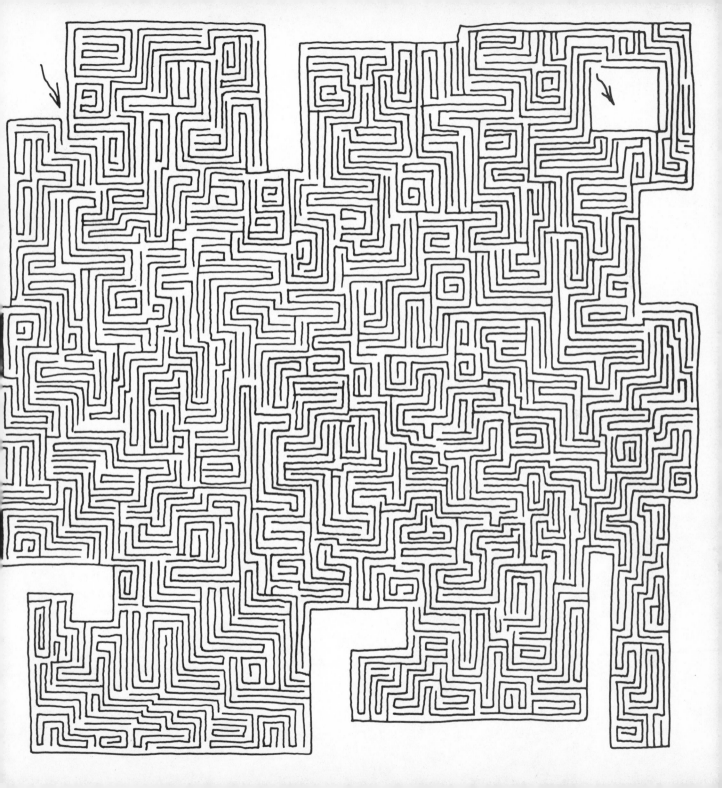

Maze 36

# SKATE

Rated Time Limit: | 38 Minutes

Maze 37
# NEEDLEPOINT
*Rated Time Limit:* | *40 Minutes*

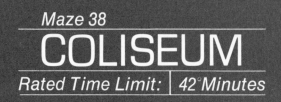

Maze 38
# COLISEUM
*Rated Time Limit:* | *42°Minutes*

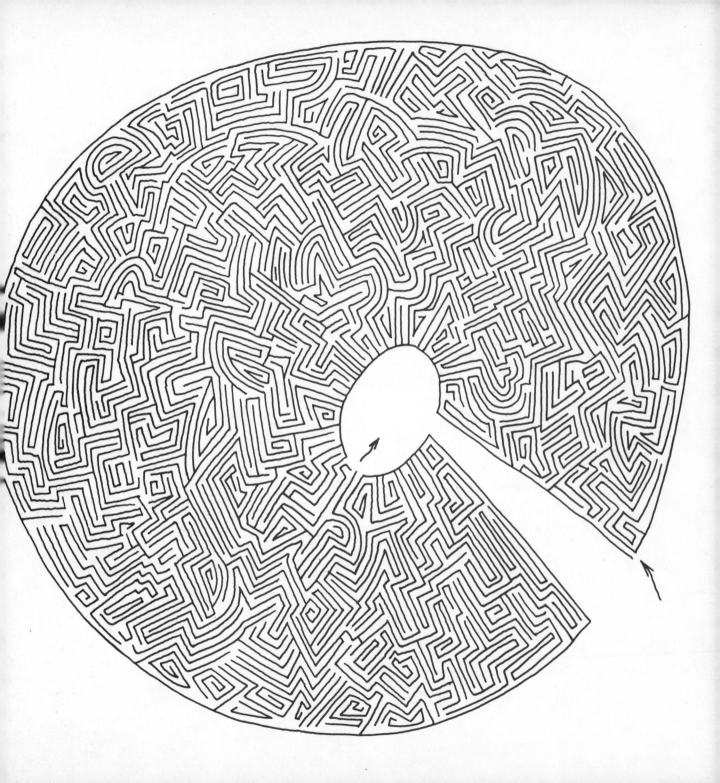

Maze 39

# BLASPHEMY

Rated Time Limit: | 45 Minutes

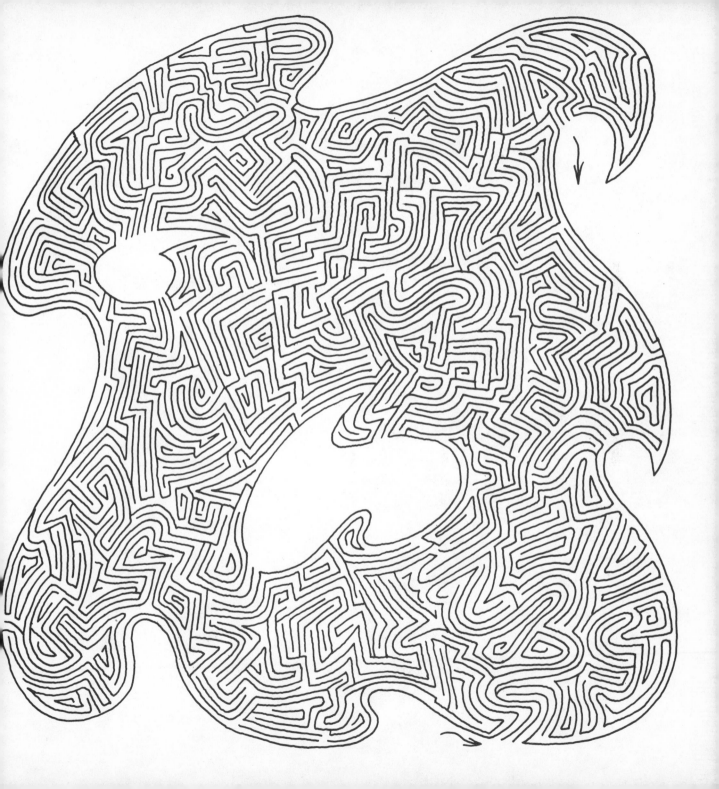

*Maze 40*

# DIEN BIEN PHU

*Rated Time Limit:* | *45 Minutes*

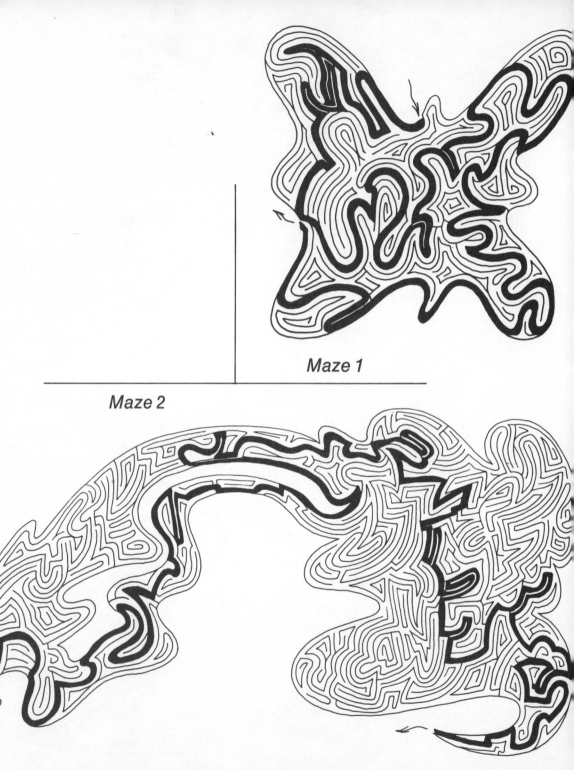

Maze 1

Maze 2

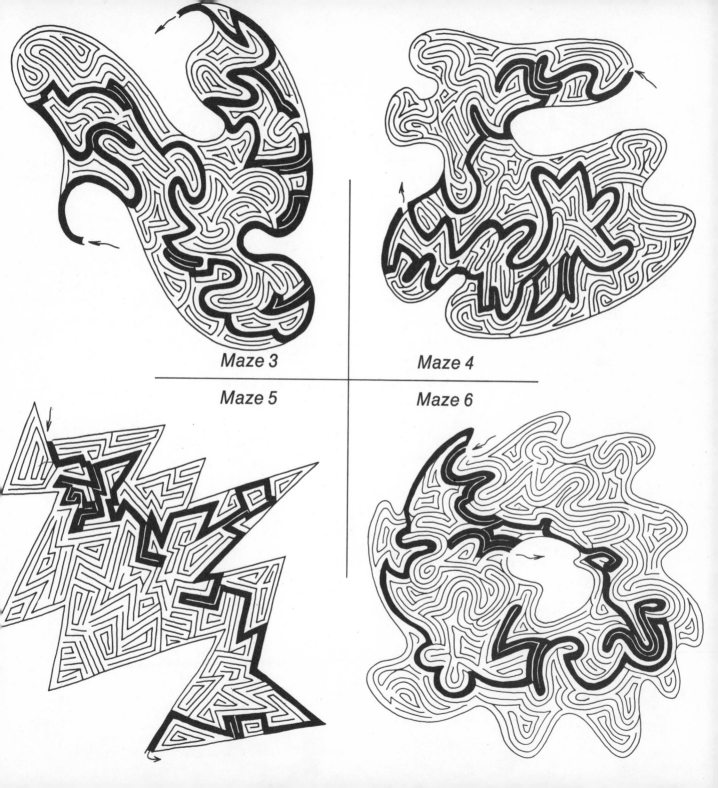

Maze 3

Maze 4

Maze 5

Maze 6

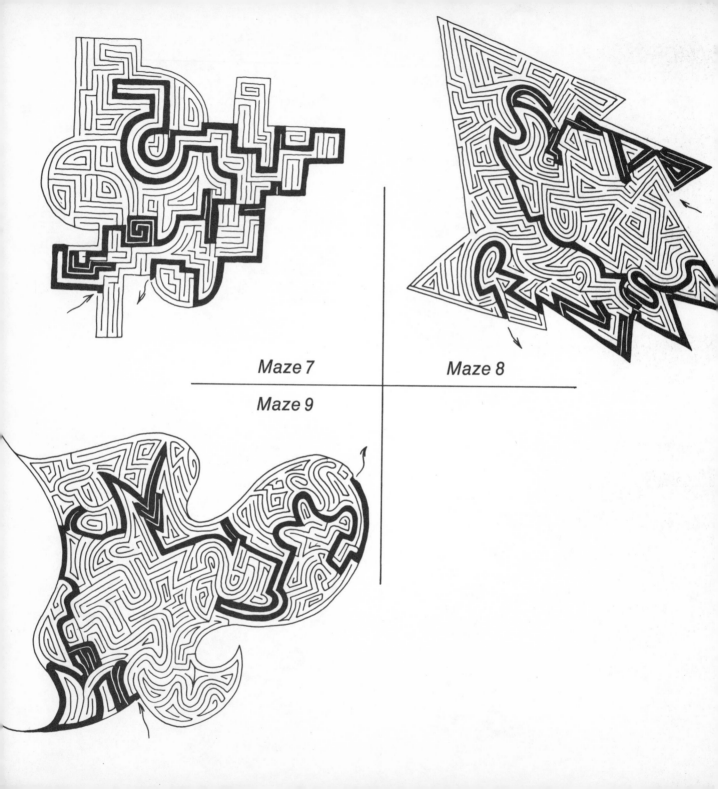

Maze 7

Maze 8

Maze 9

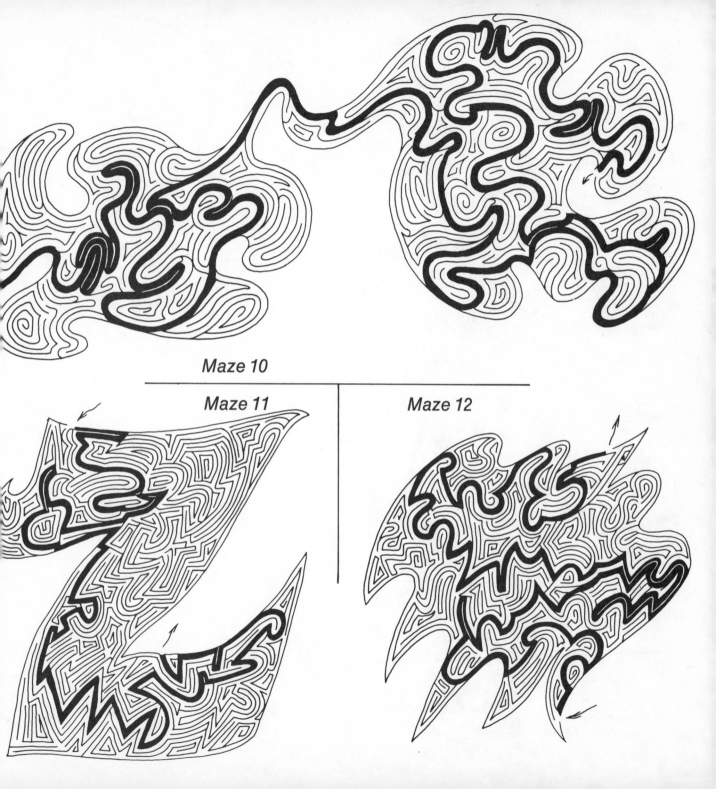

Maze 10

Maze 11

Maze 12

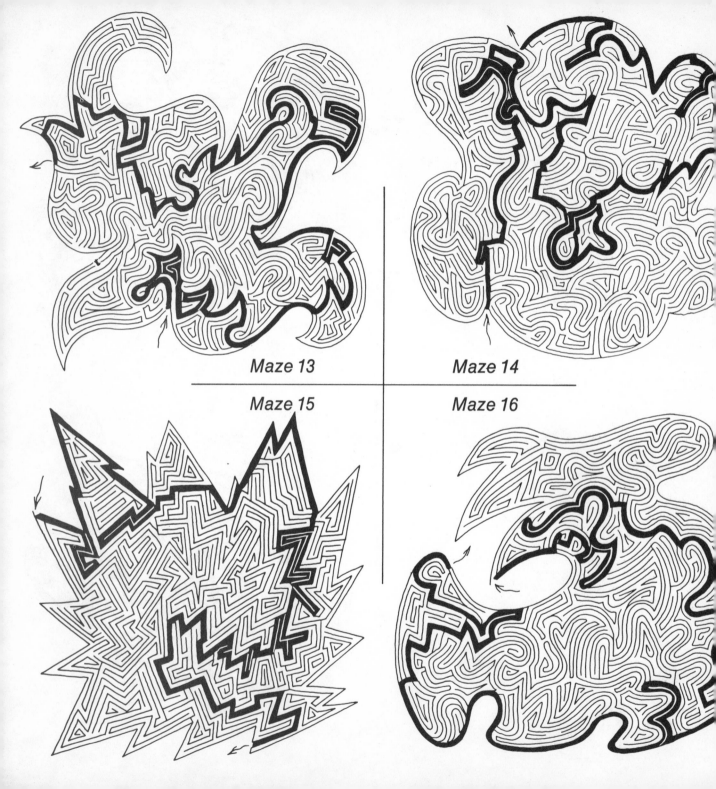

Maze 13

Maze 14

Maze 15

Maze 16

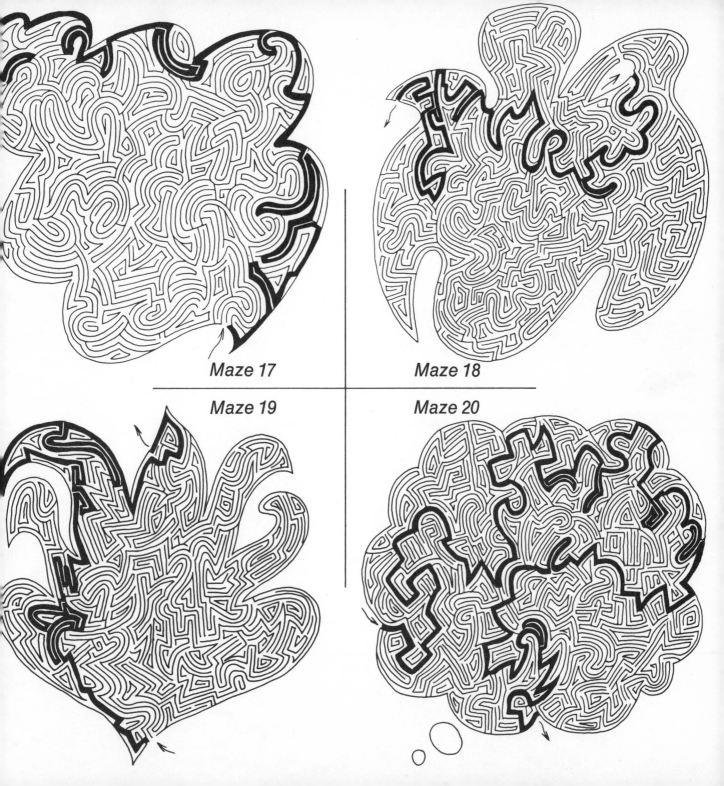

Maze 17

Maze 18

Maze 19

Maze 20

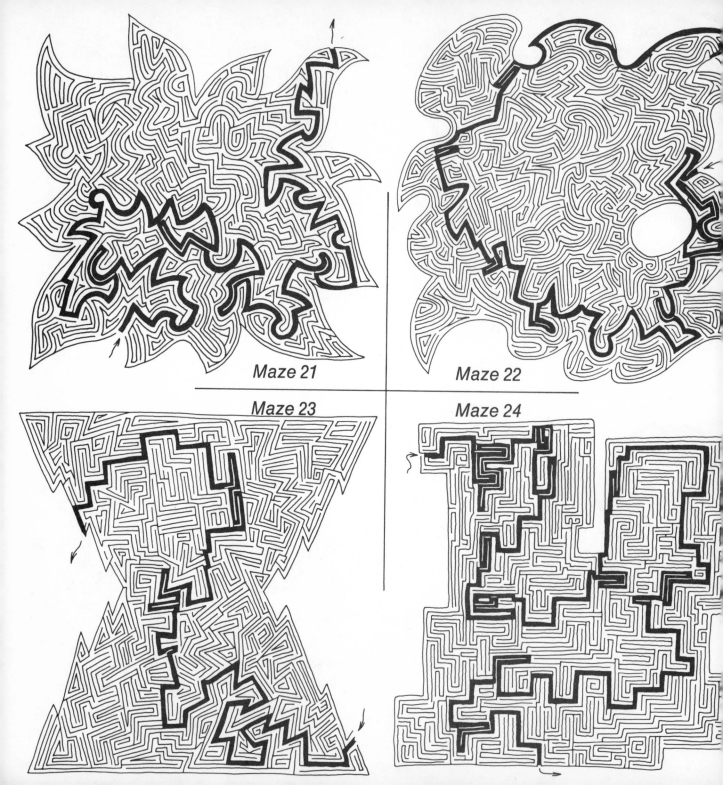

Maze 21

Maze 22

Maze 23

Maze 24

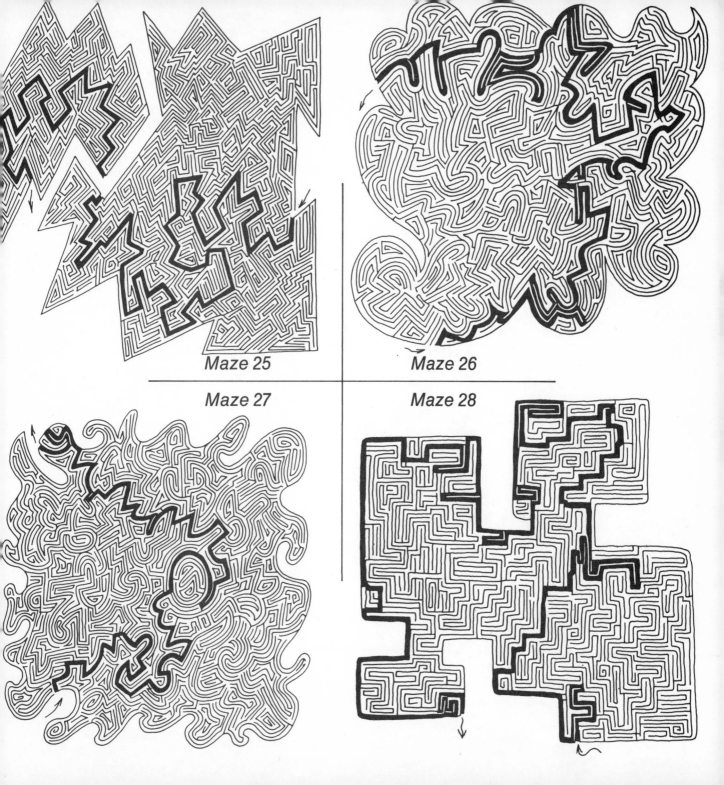

Maze 25

Maze 26

Maze 27

Maze 28

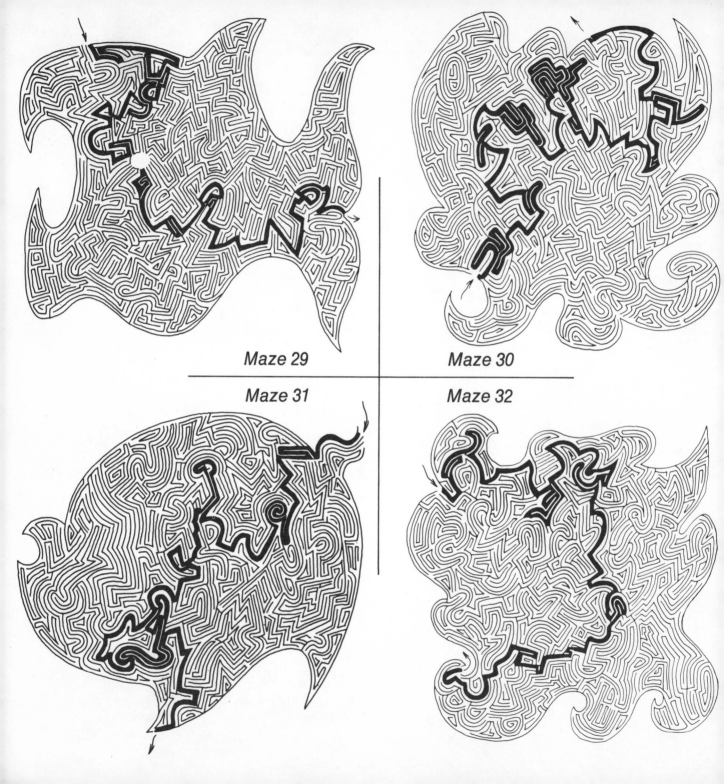

Maze 29

Maze 30

Maze 31

Maze 32

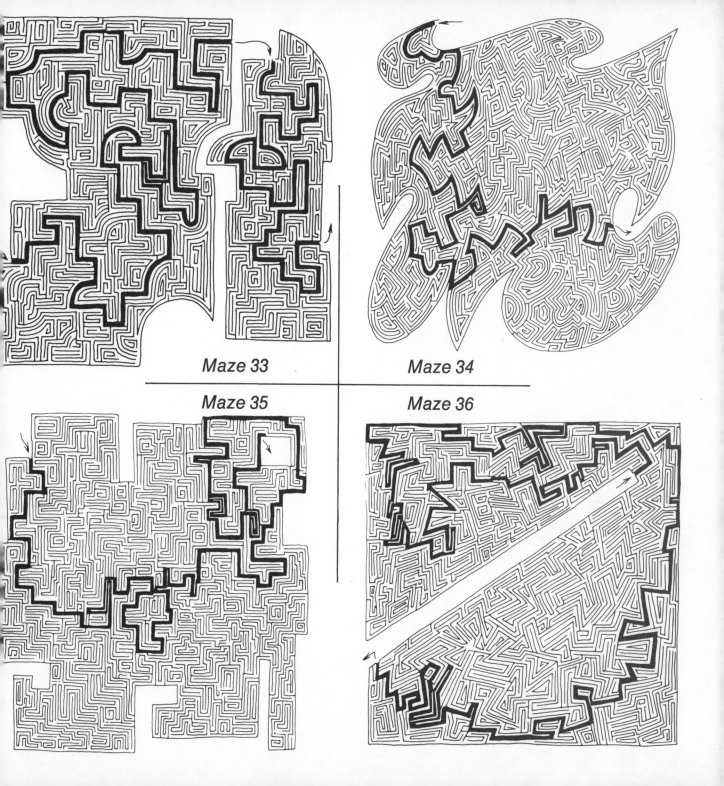

Maze 33

Maze 34

Maze 35

Maze 36

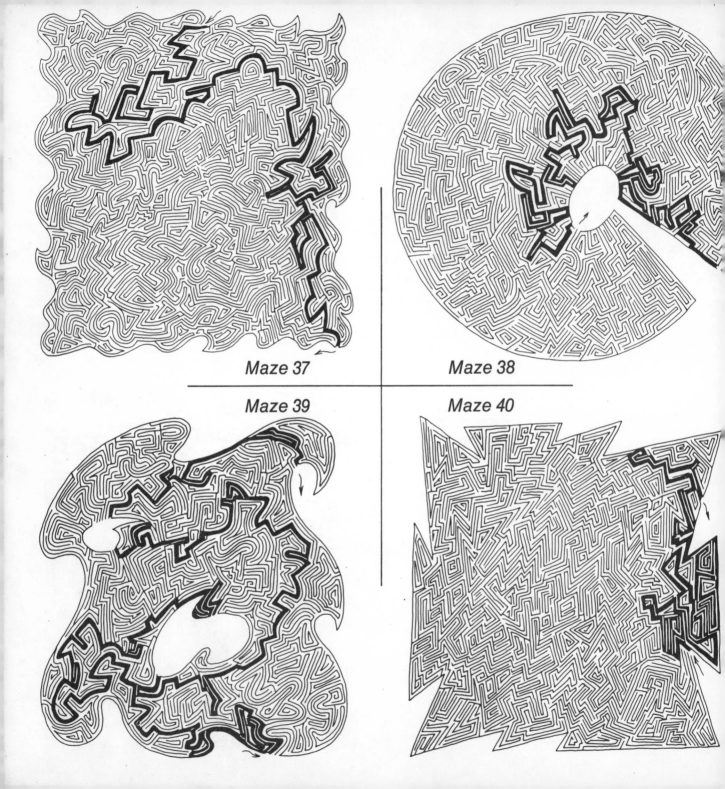

Maze 37

Maze 38

Maze 39

Maze 40